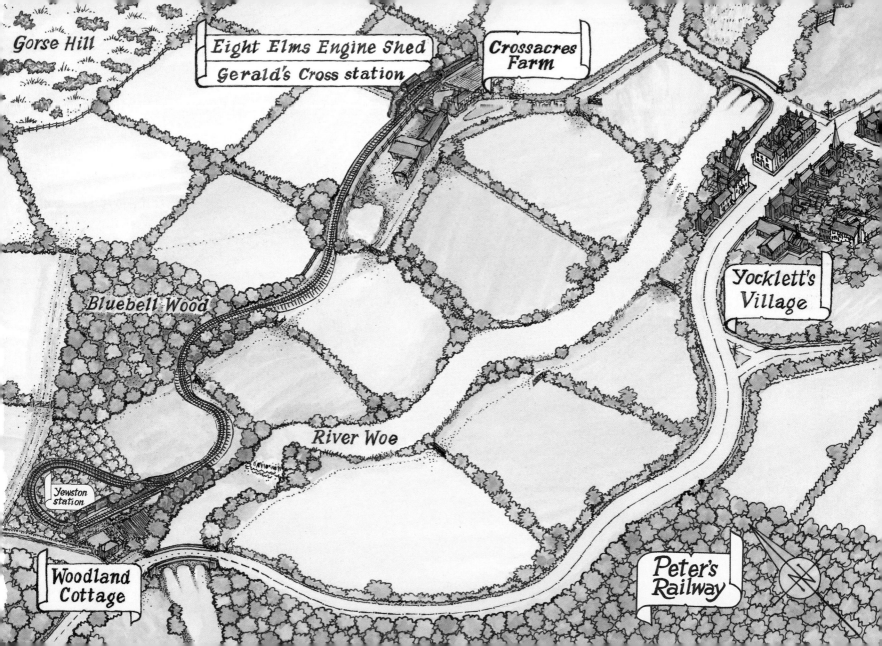

Gorse Hill

Eight Elms Engine Shed

Gerald's Cross station

Crossacres Farm

Bluebell Wood

Yocklett's Village

Yewston station

River Woe

Woodland Cottage

Peter's Railway

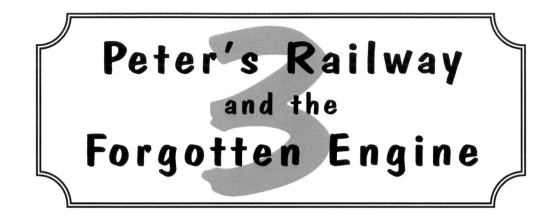

Peter's Railway and the Forgotten Engine

Published by Christopher Vine 2009

Printed by The Amadeus Press
Cleckheaton, West Yorkshire,
England.

ISBN 978-0-9553359-3-8

Foreword

In this, the third book in the series, I have tried to strike a balance between making it enjoyable for someone who has not read the previous books, and still interesting for those who have followed them all.

I receive a lot of feedback, almost all of which says how much the technical parts of the books are enjoyed. In many cases it seems that this is devoured first, with the story coming second. There are also many requests not to 'dumb them down'.

It would be easy to find lots of simple railway things to explain but that would leave out so many other fascinating machines and ideas. It would also miss the opportunity of explaining some real science and engineering principles. It seems a great shame to me that, while many young children are really interested in how things work, they often lose this enquiring nature as they grow older. I wonder if this is because science is so often simplified to the point of being boring.

The technical pages have some simple items but there are also some which are more challenging. I hope they are still clear if looked at carefully, perhaps with help from an adult.

I have always been completely fascinated with how things work, much to the frustration of my parents, who often found things had been taken to pieces and put back together defectively! I just hope these books will help to keep an interest alive in others for all things mechanical and (soon) electrical.

Chris Vine

For Grandpa Gerald.

The watercolour illustrations are by John Wardle.

Peter's Railway

It was a sunny afternoon and Peter was up at Grandpa Gerald's farm. He was getting ready to raise steam in Fiery Fox for some friends who were coming to see the railway.

As he oiled and cleaned the engine he thought to himself that he must be the luckiest boy in the world. He lives in Woodland Cottage with his Mum, Dad and the twins Kitty and Harry. Best of all, his Grandma Pat and Grandpa Gerald live on Crossacres Farm, just across the fields. Grandpa takes him on all sorts of adventures and they have also built a railway, linking their two houses across the farm. They have the use of Fiery Fox, a beautiful model of an LNER steam locomotive which Mr Esmond has kindly lent to them.

Meanwhile, Grandpa Gerald was sitting on a seat in the sun watching Peter prepare the engine. He was thinking to himself that he was probably the luckiest *Grandpa* in the world. He loves having his family living nearby, and in particular, loves sharing his passion for steam trains with young Peter. Their adventures keep him feeling young.

He tells Grandma that he is doing all these things to entertain Peter. However if the truth be known, he enjoys them just as much himself.

Between them they are quite a team!

Originally the railway was just a simple up and down track between the two stations at their houses. This worked well enough but the trains always had to run forwards one way and then backwards the other. So they built a turntable at the farm end of the line and a turning loop to run the trains round at Woodland Cottage.

Peter's little twin sister and brother, Kitty and Harry, are getting a bit older now and are definitely interested in the railway. Peter has made two little seats for them which fit into the engineers' wagon. They sit one at each end, facing each other and have little harnesses to stop them climbing out.

Peter made the seats in Grandpa's workshop one evening out of some old ply-wood sheet which was lying around. The seats can be lifted out easily so the wagon can be used again for carrying the ballast stones for any new track which they build.

The twins like nothing better than to sit in their seats riding up and down the line, watching the world go by.

Kitty and Harry also enjoy pushing their wagon up and down a bit of track near the station. In fact you could say that they used their railway wagon to learn to walk instead of the normal type of baby walker which you can buy in a shop.

This summer Peter and Grandpa have a grand plan. They are going to extend the railway to Yockletts Village, the other side of the farm.

Everyone thinks they are extending it so that Grandma can take the train into the village to do her shopping. But Peter and Grandpa have another idea which they are keeping very quiet about: The line will be nearly twice as long as before and if they build another loop of track at the far end, they will be able to run trains non-stop and very fast!

They are pretty certain that Grandma will disapprove of high speed trains. So they decide it's better if she doesn't know about that part of the plan just yet.......

Peter had lit the fire in the locomotive and it was getting good and hot by the time his friends arrived. He had already oiled all the vital moving parts of the engine and made sure that the boiler had enough water in it.

His visitors were Anna, Cara and their big brother William. They live a few miles along the valley and Peter has known them since they were very young. Considering they are brothers and sisters, their characters are quite different. Anna is bold and wants to know what everyone is doing. Cara is always interested in plants and animals and natural things like the weather. And William? Well he is always getting into trouble. Anna and Cara call him the 'naughty monkey'.

They had been driven to the farm by their Dad, Steve. He had been a farrier in the army, making and putting new shoes on all the horses in the Cavalry. He was a great big man with huge powerful arms from hammering red-hot horse shoes on the forge. With Anna and Cara he was definitely in charge. But whatever tactics he tried, William was always a bit of a tearaway.

The friends were all amazed to see how much Peter was in control of Fiery Fox. They had thought that Grandpa would do everything and Peter would only be allowed to watch.

They asked loads of questions and Peter did his best to answer them all and explain the main controls in Fiery Fox's cab. He showed them the regulator lever to make her go faster and slower, the reverser to make her go forwards or backwards and the lever which controlled the brakes. There were a lot of other levers and valves but he did not try to explain them just yet. He could do that later if they were still interested.

They watched as, little by little, the needle on the pressure gauge crept up. At last it showed 100 pounds per square inch, they were nearly ready to go. Peter just needed to fill the engine's tender with coal and water from the water barrel at the engine shed and they were all set.

The wagons were coupled up behind Fiery Fox and it was time for everyone to board the train for the first run down the line to Woodland Cottage. Minnie and Cato jumped into their special wagons and settled down for an afternoon of idle leisure.

"Hold on with both hands all the time," Grandpa told the passengers. "And don't put your feet down or try to get off until we have stopped. We don't want any accidents. Do we William?" he asked, looking him in the eye.

Grandpa knew what William was like and wanted to make sure he didn't do anything silly like trying to grab bits of tree or grass while going along. He decided to ride on the guard's van at the back of the train so he could keep an eye on him.

"Is everybody ready?" called Peter over his shoulder.

"Yes!" they all shouted back.

Peter blew a loud blast on the steam whistle and cracked open the regulator.

Very gently, Fiery Fox pulled the train out of Gerald's Cross station at Crossacres Farm.

The front of the locomotive almost disappeared in a huge cloud of steam which was coming from the drain valves. After a few yards, the cylinders were warming up nicely and Peter shut the drains and opened the regulator a little more.

Fiery Fox now started to work harder on the train and slowly they gathered speed, past the barns and alongside the pond.

Anna, Cara and William were enjoying the trip as there was plenty to see and the view kept changing. One moment they were going through a field of cows, next it was into Bluebell Wood with the line curving between the trees. And then it was out into the sunshine again, crossing a field and then charging along beside the river and the waterfall.

All too soon it was time for Peter to gently apply the locomotive's brakes and start to slow the train. They slowly rolled into Yewston station at Woodland Cottage.

The visitors didn't want to get off the train. "Keep going Peter," they shouted.

So Peter blew the whistle, opened the regulator and started off again.

The train pulled out of the station and round the loop of line through the orchard so that it ended up facing back towards the farm. It went over some points and back onto the main line for the return trip. Fiery Fox had to work much harder now as most of the line was uphill this way.

Peter put some coal into the fire while they were on the move because there wasn't time at the station. When he had first tried firing out on the line, most of it missed the firehole and spilled on the floor of the cab. He was getting better at this after quite a lot of practice and most of the coal went into the fire now. As always he kept a very watchful eye on the boiler water gauge to make sure the level didn't get too low. An explosion would spoil the whole day.

Once, when a cow was standing on the track, he blew the whistle long and loud until it jumped out of the way, only just in time. That had been a bit too close for comfort (for the cow!).

Back at the farm station, Peter uncoupled the engine, ran it round the train and turned it around on the turntable. With it facing the right way for the next run, he reversed it back onto the train and coupled up.

Grandma's Close Shave

On the next run to Woodland Cottage, Grandma was joining them. Peter's mum, Jo, had made some refreshments and Grandma was looking forward to a trip down the line and a chat with Jo.

While they waited for Grandma, Peter attached her luxurious Saloon Carriage to the train. He had to shunt some of the wagons around a little so that the guard's van was at the rear.

When they were all aboard and Grandma was safely installed in her saloon, Grandpa climbed onto the guard's van, waved to Peter and they were off.

Grandma still thought the "GW" written in gold letters on the side of her saloon stood for the Great Western railway. Luckily she had not yet heard Peter and Grandpa talking about it as the Granny Wagon. She would have been a little upset!

After an uneventful run down the line, they arrived at Peter's garden and then spent an enjoyable hour eating too many cakes and biscuits.

William, being naughty as usual, found a whole chocolate cake and hid it under a low table in the corner of the room. He planned to eat it all himself when nobody was looking. Unfortunately when he went back to it he found Minnie's tail and Kitty and Harry's feet sticking out from under the table. Minnie's tail was wagging madly as she and the twins scoffed the lot! William didn't get any.

Out in the garden again, Peter told his friends a bit more about how the engine worked and how the wagons were all coupled together. He showed them the chains which hitched onto hooks on the next wagon and also how the buffers had springs to absorb any bumps between the wagons. But soon it was time to get back on the train for the last trip of the day, back to Crossacres Farm.

Peter started off slowly round the loop and only really opened the regulator wide when he was back on the main line. Fiery Fox pulled hard on the train. They were accelerating up the long bank beside the river and then across the field.

They were still going uphill, but Peter eased back the regulator to slow down for all the bends in the track as the line went through Bluebell Wood.

He could not possibly know what was happening on the train behind him. And Grandpa could not easily see forward, round the Granny Wagon. But just then, the naughty William played a trick on them all.

As the train slowed, the coupling chains between the wagons went slack because Fiery Fox was no longer pulling hard. It was the moment William had been waiting for and he lifted the chain at the back of his wagon off its hook. The Granny Wagon (with Granny in it) and the guard's van (with Grandpa on it) were uncoupled from the front part of the train.

No one had seen him do it.

Peter, not realising what had happened, opened up Fiery Fox again to pull the train up the bank and on through the woodland.

At first, Grandma and Grandpa did not notice either. Their part of the train was still rolling forward. But they were going uphill and soon they slowed down and stopped.

Grandpa looked around the side of the Granny Wagon and realised that the train had parted in the middle, but before he could do anything about it, they started to roll back down the bank.

They moved only slowly to start with and Grandpa could easily have jumped off, but he wanted to stay close to Grandma.

"Hold on tight Dear!" he shouted to her. "That wretched William has uncoupled us and we're rolling back down the bank."

"Well put the brakes on," Grandma shouted back at him. "And stop this thing NOW!"

"There aren't any brakes," shouted back Grandpa, as the train gathered speed.

At this point in the story it should be pointed out that what Grandma shouted at Grandpa was not very polite and is best left to the reader's imagination.

Meanwhile, the front portion of the train with Peter, Anna, Cara and William, arrived at Gerald's Cross Station.

"Peter," laughed William, "where are your grandparents?"

When Peter looked round and saw the gloating look on William's face, he knew immediately what he had done.

"Get off the train at once," he shouted. "I'll have to go back and see if they're alright."

Peter was really worried. He knew that at the bottom of the long bank there was a fairly tight bend in the line, just by the river.

At the bend, the runaway train would be going at its fastest and, if it didn't make it round, it would come off the rails and fly into the river....

He let Minnie and Cato out of their wagons and then reversed the empty train as fast as he dared, in hot pursuit.

At the same time, Grandma and Grandpa were hurtling at a terrific speed towards the curve by the river.

"Lean to the left," shouted Grandpa at the top of his voice. "It will help keep us on the rails."

Like racing cyclists, they both leant to one side and shot round the curve with the inside wheels just starting to lift off the rail. Grandma's carriage felt more like a mad roller coaster than a graceful saloon.

Peter, chasing after them, saw it all happen. He held his breath and hoped for the best.

Luckily they had made the track carefully and it was very smooth. The speeding train took the curve and just managed to stay on the rails. But how far would they go before they rolled to a stop?

Peter slowed the engine down and followed them as they went into the garden at Woodland Cottage, through the station and half way round the loop.

Peter jumped off Fiery Fox and ran to see if Grandma and Grandpa were alright. By the time he reached them, Grandma had already got out of her carriage and was talking to Grandpa.

"I know it wasn't your fault Peter," she said, smiling to him, "But all the same, I think I'll walk home. It's much safer!"

"And if that naughty boy William knows what's good for him," she added grimly, "he will have gone before I get home...."

"Phew! That was a close shave," she said, using one of her funny phrases. And she set off for home on foot.

When she had gone, Peter and Grandpa quietly coupled up the two parts of the train and carefully drove it back to the farm. They put Fiery Fox back into the engine shed and let the fire go out. She could cool down slowly overnight.

Simple Brakes (not automatic)

A brake shoe (red) hangs on a swinging hanger (green). When the train is moving, the shoes are swung away from the wheel so they do not rub.

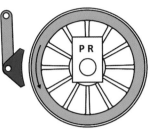

When the driver applies the brakes, the red brake shoe is pressed onto the turning wheel by a mechanism.

Friction between the moving wheel and the brake shoe slows the wheel and the train.

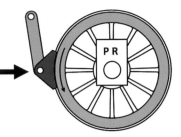

Compressed air from locomotive.

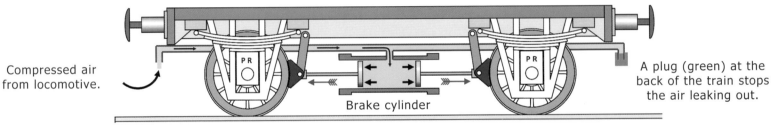

Brake cylinder

A plug (green) at the back of the train stops the air leaking out.

This wagon has simple air brakes. The brake shoes are pressed onto the wheels by compressed air (yellow) which pushes the pistons (blue) when the brakes are applied.

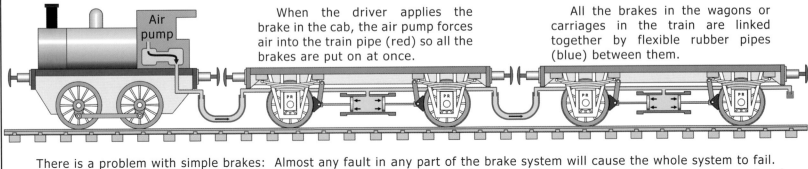

Air pump

When the driver applies the brake in the cab, the air pump forces air into the train pipe (red) so all the brakes are put on at once.

All the brakes in the wagons or carriages in the train are linked together by flexible rubber pipes (blue) between them.

There is a problem with simple brakes: Almost any fault in any part of the brake system will cause the whole system to fail. If the air pump on the locomotive fails, or if there is a leak in the pipe or the train divides (because of a broken coupling chain) and breaks one of the rubber connecting pipes: The air will leak out and the brakes won't work!

Hit the Brakes!

Back in the kitchen, Peter and Grandpa were having a cup of tea with Grandma. They were talking about the events of the day.

"I know you are going to extend the railway to Yockletts for me to do my shopping," she said. "But if you ever want me to go in that carriage again, you are going to have to fit some brakes to it."

"You're quite right," replied Grandpa. "In the early days of the full-size railways, they had plenty of accidents because the brakes were useless or not there at all. Sometimes they just had hair-raising runaways, but often they had terrible crashes."

"The trouble was," he continued, "it was expensive to fit brakes to the trains. Everyone knew they should have them, but they made all sorts of excuses and delayed fitting them for as long as possible."

"On the Highland Railway in Scotland," Grandpa remembered, "they had a terrifying runaway train. No one was hurt in the accident but it could have been a terrible disaster.

"Whatever happened?" asked Peter and Grandma.

"The date was the 25th September 1897," began Grandpa. "And it was a dark and stormy night in the Highlands of Scotland."

"Engine number 88 of the Highland Railway was hauling a heavy train from the town of Dingwall in the East, to the station of Strome Ferry on the West coast of Scotland."

"After leaving from Dingwall there was a long climb up the line and then, for two miles, there was an even steeper gradient up to a place called Raven Rock. All the time the wheels of the locomotive were slipping on the wet rails. Several times they nearly slid to a stop."

"After much huffing, puffing and rough tugging by the engine," continued Grandpa, "one of the coupling chains between the carriages broke and the rear part of the train started to roll back down the steep gradient."

"Good gracious!" said Grandma. "Whatever did they do?"

"Well that was the funny thing," replied Grandpa. "They didn't *do* anything. The Guard in the brake van at the back didn't know anything was wrong, until he realised he was travelling backwards at over 10 miles an hour. By then it was too late. His single brake on the guard's van was useless against the heavy train on a long and steep hill. They started to pick up speed quickly and soon were hurtling backwards into the night."

"It was pitch black and must have been absolutely terrifying for the passengers," he added. "Nobody really knows what speed they got up to, but I think it must have been 60 or 70 miles an hour. They rolled and lurched through a series of tight bends before finally smashing through some level crossing gates and coming to rest."

"After that accident, the railway had no option but to fit brakes to their trains," he concluded. "They were told to fit a special type called the *automatic* brake. The clever thing about them is that if anything goes wrong, the brakes are applied automatically. Even if the train splits in two, the brakes would be applied instantly to every carriage and bring it to a safe stop."

Grandma, who had been listening carefully, said "They sound just the thing. I think you had better fit automatic brakes to your railway."

Peter and Grandpa could not really argue with that and nodded their heads in agreement. They would make a start tomorrow.

The next day, Peter and Grandpa got up early and went out to the workshop as soon as they had finished breakfast. The first thing they did was to light a fire in the stove.

The stove was a recent addition to the workshop which Grandpa had installed during the winter. He had found it in a skip outside a house down the road and could immediately see how useful it would be. It kept the place lovely and warm, even on a cold winter's day.

As well as keeping the workshop warm, it had a hot plate on the top which could be used to boil a kettle. It also had a little oven at the side where Grandpa could cook baked potatoes for his lunch, if ever Grandma went out for the day.

Once the fire was roaring and the workshop was getting cosy, Grandpa started to explain:

"Brakes on a train work in much the same way as the brakes on a bicycle. Brake blocks are pushed by a mechanism onto the outside of the wheels when the brakes are applied. As the turning wheels rub against the brake blocks, they are slowed down by friction. On a train the blocks are called brake *shoes*, and they are made of metal instead of rubber, but the principle is just the same."

"It will be quite a lot of work to make all the parts and then fit them to all the carriages," he said. "But it will be much safer afterwards."

They didn't mind that it took them a whole week, it was horrible weather anyway. In fact it was enjoyable work because it wasn't very difficult and they kept the stove going the whole time. With the howling wind and rain outside and the warm fug inside, they were quite content.

When the brakes were finished, it was time to try them out to see if they were effective. The next fine day they raised steam in Fiery Fox and coupled up all the wagons behind her.

They didn't want any passengers on the train during their brake trials. Something might go wrong and the whole idea was to make it safer, not to put people at risk.

Instead, they loaded up the train with concrete blocks to simulate the weight of the passengers. It would make the tests more realistic.

First they tested the brakes at slow speed. Peter pushed the brake lever in the cab of Fiery Fox and was amazed at how much more quickly the train slowed down. Of course, all the wheels on the train were helping to stop it now and not just the wheels on the engine and tender. In fact to bring it to a gentle stop, he had to move the brake lever much less.

Now it was time to really test the brakes - at high speed. They would do a controlled scientific experiment by measuring and timing how quickly the train stopped; first with the new brakes working and again with the new brakes disconnected.

They found a good level part of the railway and put a stake in the ground beside the track, as a marker. When they passed this marker post, Peter would slam on the brakes.

Taking a good run up, Peter opened the regulator and Fiery Fox pulled hard on the train. Faster and faster they went.

They were going at a terrific speed when they got to the post. Peter hit the brakes and, with a toot on the whistle, Grandpa started timing with his watch.

When the train had screeched to a halt, he checked the time. They had stopped in just 10 seconds. Then they got off and walked back along the track, counting out the paces, back to the marker post. They had stopped in less than 50 metres.

"That was incredible", said Peter. "Now for the test with the new train brakes disconnected. We will see what the difference is by just using the old brakes on the engine and tender."

They reversed the train and got ready for their second charge up the line. Again Peter put the brakes on when they got to the post, but this time it was only the brakes on the engine and tender which were working.

The difference was quite obvious. The train slowed down quite gently and it took a full 30 seconds to stop. When they paced out the distance it was well over 150 metres this time. The new brakes were certainly effective.

There was however, one last test to do before they could report to Grandma that the brakes were a complete success. They reconnected the new brakes and set off to Woodland Cottage to simulate William's prank.

They went round the loop and, half way up the long hill, Peter eased back the regulator. This time it was Grandpa who uncoupled the rear part of the train.

What would happen? Would the brakes work automatically?

As the train split in two, the little rubber vacuum pipe which connected the brakes from one wagon to the next, pulled off its connector. Air rushed into the pipe and the brakes on the engine and all of the wagons slammed on instantly.

Fiery Fox went on a little way before the brakes stopped her, but the rear half of the train with the Granny Wagon rolled to a stop very quickly. This time, instead of rolling backwards, the brakes held it safely on the hill.

Now, quite satisfied that the brakes were working perfectly, they put the train away and went in to tell Grandma.

"We have tested the brakes in a most scientific manner," pronounced Peter seriously. "And we would like to assure you that you will never again be stuck in a runaway Granny Wagon."

Ooops! It was too late…

Peter had called it the Granny Wagon and Grandma had heard him.

"Is that what you call it behind my back?" she asked, drawing herself up to her full height and looking at him sternly.

Then she started to shake and Peter and Grandpa both thought she was very angry and upset.

But suddenly she started to roar with laughter.

"You mean to tell me that 'GW' stands for Granny Wagon and not Great Western?" she gasped between giggles.

"You're cheeky monkeys, the pair of you!"

Page 29

Automatic Brakes and the Fail-Safe Principle

In the simple brake system shown on page 20, the brakes were applied by compressed, high pressure air. The locomotive forces compressed air into the train pipe when the driver applies the brakes. This high pressure air pushes the pistons which push the brake shoes onto the wheels to slow down the train.

Any failure of the brake equipment means the brakes won't work. The system fails dangerously and something better is needed.

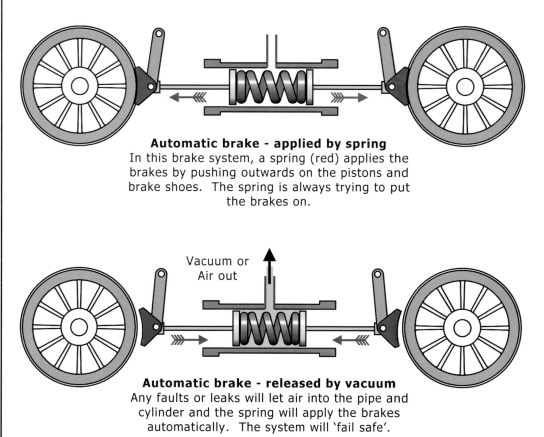

Automatic brake - applied by spring
In this brake system, a spring (red) applies the brakes by pushing outwards on the pistons and brake shoes. The spring is always trying to put the brakes on.

Vacuum or Air out

Automatic brake - released by vacuum
Any faults or leaks will let air into the pipe and cylinder and the spring will apply the brakes automatically. The system will 'fail safe'.

This is a version of an automatic brake system. It is now the spring (red) which applies the brakes.

The spring will always be trying to apply the brakes unless something squeezes the spring and pulls the brake shoes away from the wheels.

It is possible that one spring may snap, but all the other springs in the other wagons will still be working.

To release and keep the brakes released, a vacuum is used to 'pull' the pistons together, against the spring.

It doesn't matter if there is a fault on the locomotive, or a leak in the train pipe, or if the train parts and pulls a connecting pipe off. Air from the atmosphere will rush in to fill the vacuum and the spring will put the brakes on and stop the train safely.

This is a good example of a 'fail-safe' system.

What is a Vacuum?

A vacuum does not really exist: It is an empty space with nothing in it, not even air. Its pressure is very low and a perfect vacuum has zero pressure.

Looking at this diagram, most people would say that the vacuum (green) sucks the pistons together to squeeze the spring. But this is wrong. A vacuum is nothing, it doesn't exist, so how can it do anything?

The answer is that the ordinary pressure of the atmosphere (blue arrows) or air (blue) all around us is what pushes the pistons together.

The air in the atmosphere has a pressure of around 15 pounds per square inch (or 1 bar in proper metric units). You just don't notice it because it is all around you and always there.

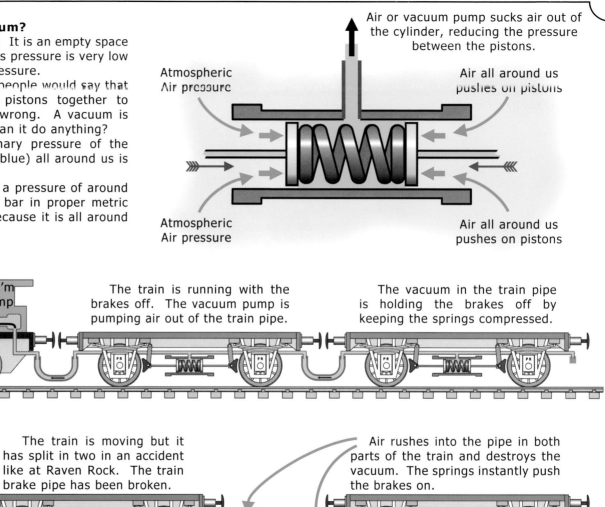

Air or vacuum pump sucks air out of the cylinder, reducing the pressure between the pistons.

Atmospheric Air pressure

Air all around us pushes on pistons

Atmospheric Air pressure

Air all around us pushes on pistons

The train is running with the brakes off. The vacuum pump is pumping air out of the train pipe.

The vacuum in the train pipe is holding the brakes off by keeping the springs compressed.

Vac'm pump

The train is moving but it has split in two in an accident like at Raven Rock. The train brake pipe has been broken.

Air rushes into the pipe in both parts of the train and destroys the vacuum. The springs instantly push the brakes on.

This is an example of a fail-safe system. The pipe has been broken (or the vacuum pump could have failed) but the brakes on all of the train come on immediately and bring it to a safe stop.

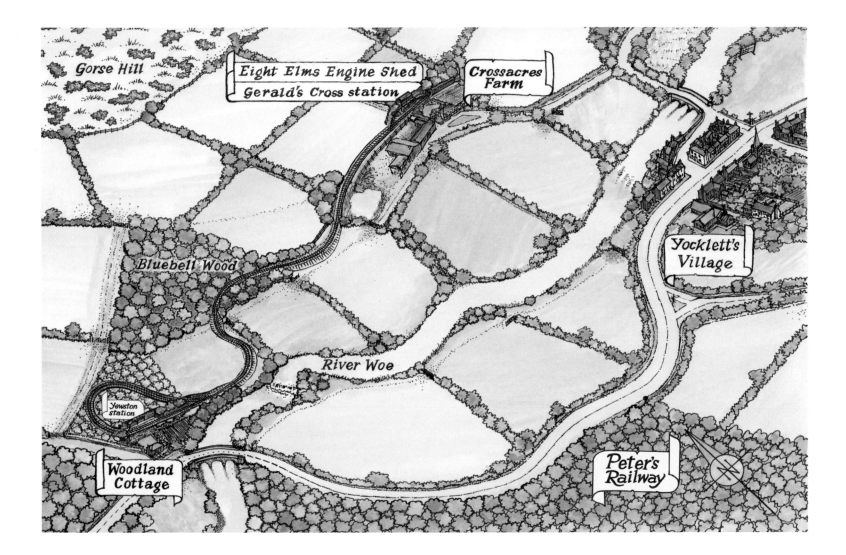

Gorse Hill

Eight Elms Engine Shed
Gerald's Cross station

Crossacres Farm

Yocklett's Village

Bluebell Wood

River Woe

Yewston station

Woodland Cottage

Peter's Railway

Surveying the Yockletts Extension

Surveying the ground for a railway is an important part of building it. The idea is to find the easiest route which avoids difficult obstacles like steep gradients or the need for bridges or tunnels. On a full-size railway, another important thing to consider is how the railway can pass through as many large towns as possible to maximise the amount of passengers and freight carried.

Clearly the extension was going to have to start at Gerald's Cross station, cross the drive and go over or around some fields. The end of the line would be in the field beside the bridge over the River Woe.

"Can we build a bridge over the river?" asked Peter. "It would be great if the end station was right in the middle of the village."

"It's a lovely idea," said Grandpa imagining it, "but it would be just too expensive. We would need an awful lot of material to make the bridge and anyway, I don't own the land in the middle of the village. People might complain if we put a railway through their gardens."

Peter could see his point. They would just have to make do with walking over the existing road bridge.

When they walked over the ground, they could see there was quite a large drop from the level area at the farm down to the river where they would make their end station. It would be a good idea to make the line long and curvy so that it could drop down on a gentle gradient. If they took too straight a line it would make it rather steep and Fiery Fox would struggle to pull a heavy train back up to the farm.

One obstacle which they had to cross was the drive from the public road up to the house. After looking at digging a tunnel or building a bridge, they decided on a level crossing. It would have gates which would normally be swung across the railway but, when trains were running, they could be shut across the drive to prevent any collisions with cars.

Once they had worked out the rough line the railway would follow, it was time to start looking at the different parts of it more carefully.

The first thing to decide was how to get a good route through Gerald's Cross station and past the engine shed. It would need to be carefully laid out so as not to use up too much of Grandma's garden and also to allow the trains to run through at high speed if they didn't need to stop there.

After looking at all the buildings and track, they decided to put a set of points just after the station and then run the track along the side of the engine shed. They would need just a narrow strip along the edge of Grandma's vegetable patch and the only thing which would need to be moved was a water butt.

That evening they asked Grandma if she would mind losing a little strip from her vegetable patch.

"No, I don't mind at all," she said. "In fact, that bit of ground doesn't grow very much since you built the engine shed. It keeps the sun off and makes it too shady for things to grow properly."

"Perhaps you can find a little bit of ground somewhere else for me?" she asked. "That is if you still want me to grow lots of nice vegetables for you."

Peter and Grandpa both loved the fresh vegetables that came from the garden, so they instantly agreed. They might even find her a bigger area and try to persuade her to grow raspberries which they loved.

The next day they went out, armed with some stakes, a sledgehammer, a plank and spirit level. They knocked the stakes into the ground to mark out the route. The spirit level and plank were used to make sure the tops of the stakes were nice and level so they could use them as a guide when digging out the track bed.

Down by the river they had decided to put in a turning loop, like the one at Woodland Cottage. They just had to work out where to put it so as not to get in the way of farming the field.

"I think we could run the loop right round the edge of the field," said Peter, standing by the river. "Then it would not get in the way at all."

"That's a good idea," Grandpa agreed with him. "I had not thought of that. We'll just lose a little bit of the field at the corners where the track curves round."

That evening back at the farm, Peter drew a little map of the route of the new line.

When Peter showed the map to Grandpa, they both noticed how curvy the new line would be.

"It is a bit of a shame," said Peter, "we won't be able to go very fast with all these bends."

Grandpa thought for a bit and then said "I think we could get around that problem by banking or tilting the track over a bit so that the trains will lean into the bends."

"They do exactly the same thing on the full-size railways," he explained. "But they have a special word for it; they call it *super-elevation*."

"Why don't they just call it banking?" asked Peter. "It seems such a complicated word for such a simple thing."

"Well, that's a very good question," smiled Grandpa. "I think some people just like to use long words because no one else will know what they are talking about."

"And that," he suddenly exclaimed, "is just what we are going to do...."

"If Grandma hears us talking about banking on the bends," he explained, "she will realise exactly what we are up to. 'Running express trains is much too dangerous' she'll tell us."

"So from now on," Grandpa decided, "we will not mention banking again. We'll just talk about super-elevation!"

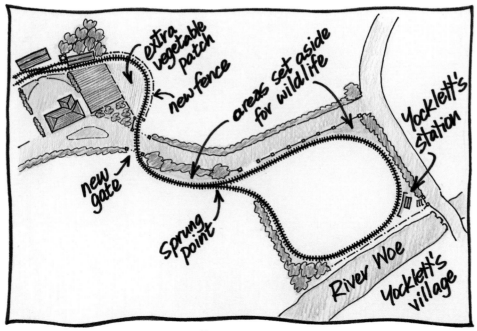

The Forgotten Engine

Bright and early next morning, Grandpa and Peter were up and about on the farm. They wanted to clear out the junk from the old barn. It would make a good storage space for all the rail and sleepers and other bits and pieces they would need for the project.

For years, the barn had been used as a dumping ground for all sorts of things which Grandpa had not wanted to throw away, but did not have a use for.

There were old bits of farm machinery, derelict bits of furniture and some worn out tyres from a tractor. The tyres were so old that the rubber had perished and was all cracking up. They were completely useless now.

They dragged the junk outside, into a huge pile which could be taken away for recycling in a few days time. Then Peter fetched a yard brush and swept the concrete floor to get it all nice and clean for the first time in many years.

Going back into the barn, Peter noticed something strange. "Look Grandpa," he said, pointing. "There is something very odd about that wall."

"What do you mean?" asked Grandpa. It looked quite normal to him.

"All the other walls are made of brick," explained Peter, "but this back wall is wood. Just old planks, nailed together."

"How very observant of you," said Grandpa. "I'm sure all the walls on the outside are made of brick. Let's go and have a look"

"It seems to me," he said, looking puzzled, "that the inside of the barn is rather smaller than the outside. I had never noticed it before, but now it seems quite obvious."

When Peter had noticed the wooden wall inside, it had not seemed very exciting, just curious. Now though, his eyes were wide with excitement.

"Do you think there might be a secret room in the barn, behind that wooden wall?" he asked, almost jumping up and down with excitement.

"Hold on a moment!" said Grandpa. "Before we get too carried away, let's measure the inside and outside of the barn very roughly by pacing it out and counting our steps."

Walking along the outside of the barn, they found it was 40 paces, but when they did the same inside, it was less than 30. The secret room, if there was one, was huge. It was amazing no one had noticed before.

"There's only one thing to do," said Grandpa, "we'll have to pull some of the planks away and see what's behind."

They went to the workshop and found a large hammer and a bar of metal to lever off some of the planks. What was in the room? Would it be something valuable, useful or interesting? More likely it would just be empty or full of old junk.

After a few minutes work, they had pulled away several planks and could look through.

They had kicked up quite a lot of dust but there was a small window, high up in the roof and what they saw in the gloom was better than anything they could possibly have hoped for.

Sitting there was a steam traction engine. She was rather dusty but seemed to be complete. In the dim light they could just make out her name. A plate on the side of her boiler declared: "Mighty Atom".

Quickly they pulled away more of the wood and made a hole large enough to clamber through.

There were some other old bits of machinery in the room, but Peter and Grandpa only had eyes for the traction engine.

She was very big, with two huge rear driving wheels and smaller ones at the front. They didn't have any rubber tyres on them, just strips of metal to grip on the earth or road. At least metal tyres did not get punctures or perish and go flat over the years.

Hanging from the metal steering wheel, was a leather satchel. What could be in it?

Peter climbed up to get the satchel and opened it. Inside were some papers, drawings and an envelope addressed to "The future owner of Crossacres Farm."

He handed it to Grandpa, who cut it open with his pen knife. Then he read it out:

"Dear Finder,

Please take care of the Mighty Atom. She has been a faithful engine to me over the years. I find her less useful now that I have bought a diesel tractor, but I cannot bear to see her broken up for scrap. To save her for the future, I am putting her into storage out of harm's way in this barn. I have greased the works and drained and dried the boiler so I have done all I can. Take care of her for me. Sincerely yours George Porter. 4th March 1941."

From the excitement of a few minutes ago, Grandpa and Peter were now slightly overcome and could hardly speak.

When they had recovered a little from reading the letter, they set to work and pulled down the rest of the timber wall. Then, using the modern tractor, they pulled the Mighty Atom out of her hiding place and had a good look at her.

It was clear that Mr Porter had done exactly as he'd said. Mighty Atom was dirty but otherwise in excellent condition. Grandpa climbed onto her and, putting both hands on the rim of the flywheel, pulled hard.

Slowly the flywheel moved round and they could see all the works of the engine moving. The crank, connecting rod, piston rod and valve gear, all seemed to be in perfect working order after being stored away for over 60 years.

Grandpa explained that traction engines were used to pull things and also to drive stationary machines. Unlike railway engines, they had gears between the engine part and the rear wheels which meant they could pull very heavy loads, but quite slowly.

He also showed Peter how the gears could be disengaged so the engine and flywheel could turn without turning the back wheels. This was done when driving machinery with a belt from the flywheel.

"Nowadays," Grandpa finished, "almost all machines have their own electric motor or diesel engine to drive them. But years ago, farms did not have mains electricity and diesel engines were very heavy and expensive."

Peter wanted to fill the boiler and light the fire straight away, but Grandpa calmed him down.

"The one thing we will have to get checked," he said, "is the boiler."

"I know the previous owner said he had dried it out, but we can't take any risks with a boiler as big as this," he explained. "If it has gone rusty inside, the plates may not be strong enough to hold the pressure of the steam. An explosion would be too horrific to even think about."

"I'll go indoors and telephone a boiler inspector I know. He will be able to do a thorough examination and tell us if she is still safe to steam."

While Grandpa was indoors, Peter went to find lots of old rags and started to wipe off the years of muck and dust. He then went into their engine shed to get some metal polish to clean up the nameplate so that it shone in the sunlight.

In no time at all he had her gleaming.

"You won't have to wait long," called Grandpa, returning from the house. "He's coming tomorrow morning."

Peter was going to find it very difficult to get to sleep that night. What would the inspector find? Would Mighty Atom's boiler be safe or would it have rusted beyond repair?

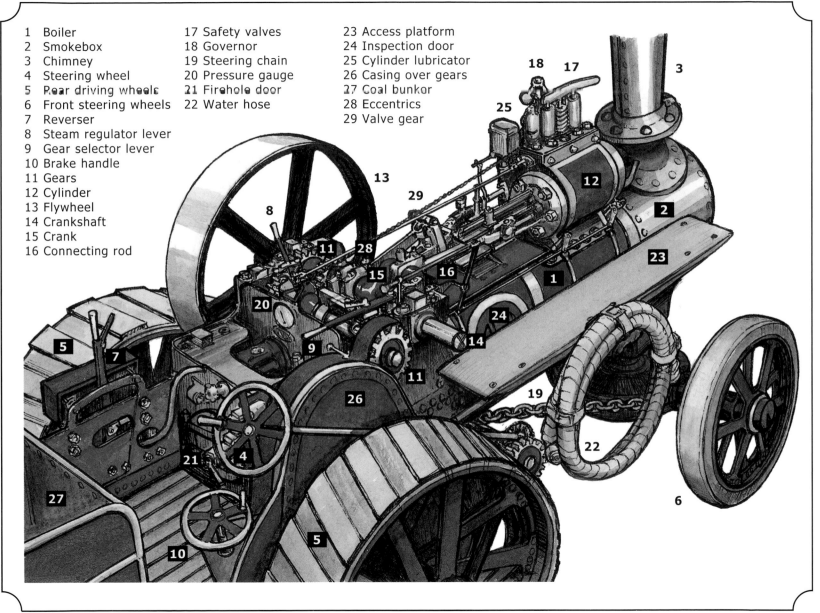

1 Boiler
2 Smokebox
3 Chimney
4 Steering wheel
5 Rear driving wheels
6 Front steering wheels
7 Reverser
8 Steam regulator lever
9 Gear selector lever
10 Brake handle
11 Gears
12 Cylinder
13 Flywheel
14 Crankshaft
15 Crank
16 Connecting rod

17 Safety valves
18 Governor
19 Steering chain
20 Pressure gauge
21 Firehole door
22 Water hose

23 Access platform
24 Inspection door
25 Cylinder lubricator
26 Casing over gears
27 Coal bunker
28 Eccentrics
29 Valve gear

Gears and Gear Ratios

Gears can be used to transmit power from one rotating shaft to another.
They are usually made of metal and have teeth which lock together or 'mesh' so that one gear turns the other.

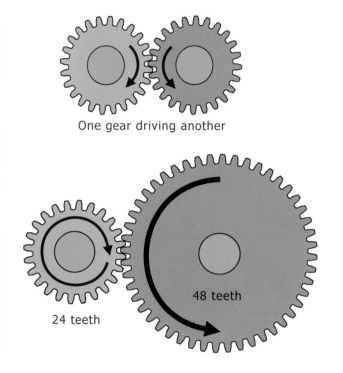

One gear driving another

The blue gear is on the drive shaft of a motor for example. It is turning or driving the pink gear because the teeth of the two gears are locking or 'meshing' together.

The blue gear is turning in one direction (clockwise) and the driven gear is turning in the other direction (anticlockwise).

The two gears are the same size and have the same number of teeth so they are rotating at the same speed but in opposite directions.

48 teeth

24 teeth

Here the two gears are different sizes. The small one has 24 teeth and the large one has twice as many, with 48 teeth.

As the small gear turns once, its 24 teeth will push 24 teeth of the large gear; or half of its teeth. So the large gear only rotates through half a turn.

If the small gear turns two times, the large gear will turn only once. It doesn't matter how many times the small gear turns, it will always turn twice as many times as the large gear.

The speed at which one gear turns compared with the other, is usually called the gear 'ratio'.

In the first picture they both turn at the same speed and the gear ratio is 1 to 1 (Usually written 1 : 1)

In the second picture the small gear turns at twice the speed of the large gear and the gear ratio is 2 : 1

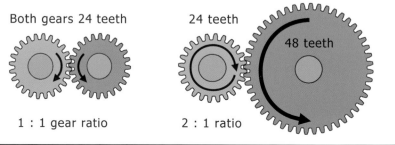

Both gears 24 teeth

24 teeth

48 teeth

1 : 1 gear ratio

2 : 1 ratio

Gear Ratios and Turning Force or 'Torque'

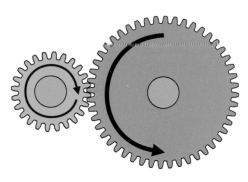

Small gear
High speed
Low turning force

Large gear
Low speed
High turning force

Gear ratios are very useful in machines because they do something else as well as changing the speed at which different shafts rotate: They change the amount of twisting or turning force in the shafts.

This twisting of turning force is called 'torque', (pronounced like talk).

With the two gears here, the large gear turns half as fast as the small one. But its turning force or torque is twice as large as that of the small gear.

There is nothing magic about the increase in the turning force in the large gear, it has just gone up as its speed has gone down.

A high turning force or torque, turning the back wheels of a traction engine enables it to pull very heavy loads.

A Train of Gears

For large gear ratios, a train of gears can be used with a double or 'compound' gear.

Here the blue gear on the motor or engine drive shaft is spinning fast and driving the pink gear at half the speed.

Then the same reduction happens again with the red gear driving the yellow gear which now goes at half the speed of the red/pink gear.

Overall, the yellow gear goes at a quarter of the speed of the blue one. However it has four times the turning force or torque of the motor or engine.

The gear ration between the blue and yellow gears is 4 : 1

This is the sort of reduction gearing used between the crank shaft of Mighty Atom and the back wheels.

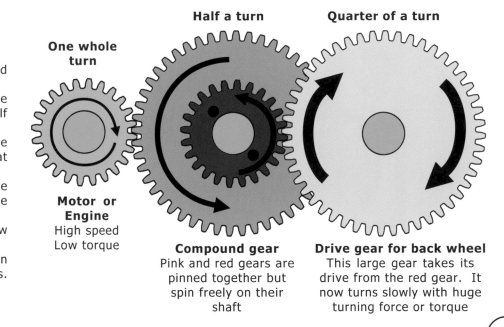

One whole turn

Motor or Engine
High speed
Low torque

Half a turn

Compound gear
Pink and red gears are pinned together but spin freely on their shaft

Quarter of a turn

Drive gear for back wheel
This large gear takes its drive from the red gear. It now turns slowly with huge turning force or torque

An Inspector Calls

Mr Tappit the boiler inspector arrived at nine o'clock sharp. After a cup of tea and a chat, the first thing he did was to unbolt a large cover plate so he could see inside the boiler.

"She looks good at a first glance," he said. "But that doesn't mean much. The real test comes when I start to measure the thickness of all the metal plates to see how much they have rusted away."

It took him a long time and he was very thorough. For Peter it seemed like forever as he was desperate to know the verdict on the boiler.

"You're very lucky," he said smiling at last. "Whoever put this engine into storage, did a superb job of it. She's in really good condition inside."

"Can we use her now?" asked Peter, who could hardly wait to light the fire.

"Hold your horses a moment, young man," said Mr Tappit. "The next thing I must check is that the metal is still strong enough. I am going to fill the boiler with water, right up to the brim. Then I am going to pump it up to pressure and see what happens."

He filled the boiler from a hose pipe and then connected a special hand pump and started to pump in more water. The more he pumped, the more the pressure went up.

Would the old metal hold tight?

When the pressure was even higher than Mighty Atom's full working pressure, Mr Tappit stopped pumping and looked all over the boiler for leaks.

"That's fine," he said at last, and let the pressure down again slowly.

The last thing to do was to carry out the steam test, to make sure the safety valves and all the other boiler fittings were working correctly.

They drained some of the water out of the boiler so the level was correct. At last it was time to light the fire in Mighty Atom for the first time in more than sixty years.

Peter put some old oily rags onto the grate in the firebox and lit them with a match. Then, as the flames got going, he added some sticks of dry wood and then coal, little by little.

While the fire was getting hotter, they oiled the works and could feel the boiler warming. Eventually the water started to boil and the pressure gauge began to creep up.

Mr Tappit made some adjustments to the safety valves so they lifted at exactly 180 pounds per square inch, Mighty Atom's working pressure.

Finally he signed a piece of paper which he handed to Grandpa. "Congratulations," he said. "Mighty Atom has passed her boiler inspection. You can put her back to work."

Grandpa put the gears into neutral, opened the drain valves and cracked open the regulator. Very slowly, and with a quiet wheezing sound, the flywheel started to turn. Mighty Atom was coming back to life.

After warming her up for a while, Grandpa said "Jump up Peter, it's time to try driving her. I'll control the engine and the brakes. You do the steering!"

Peter held onto the heavy steering wheel and they slowly started off. There was a terrific noise as all the gears clattered and clashed together. They drove into a field of grass where there was room to practice steering and getting used to the controls.

"I have just had a good idea," said Grandpa when they had stopped. "Let's hitch up a trailer and drive her to the pub for lunch. We can put some bales of straw on for seats and then take Mr Tappit and Grandma as well."

Driving down the roads to the pub was great fun. They noticed the cars going in the opposite direction either ignored them completely or pointed and stared. Some drivers almost drove into the ditch, trying to avoid the huge and noisy machine.

"The drivers of those cars are a bit like the cows in the field, the first time we drove the train past them," laughed Peter. He was enjoying every moment of this trip. The steering was very heavy, but luckily Mighty Atom's top speed was only around 10 miles an hour so there was not too much danger.

While they were having lunch at the pub, Grandpa and Peter kept a close watch on Mighty Atom. Every now and again they put a few lumps of coal on the fire and topped up the boiler with water.

When there was a quiet moment, Grandpa told them the story of the 'Puffing Devil'.

"A long time ago, in 1801," he started, "a brilliant Cornishman, Richard Trevithick built the first successful steam road locomotive. He called it the Puffing Devil."

"On the first test it ran amazingly well until it hit a ditch and broke down. The operators all went into a pub to celebrate the success of their engine with a slap up meal and some drinks. Unfortunately they were enjoying themselves rather too much and they forgot all about the Puffing Devil."

"Outside, her fire was still burning," continued Grandpa, "and the water level was getting dangerously low. Eventually the boiler blew up with a terrific bang and that was the end of that!"

After lunch they drove back to Crossacres Farm, put Mighty Atom away in the barn and wiped her down. They left her sizzling quietly while she cooled off.

Mr Tappit wished them "happy steaming" and went off home.

The Boiler, Steam and Pressure Gauge

The coal fire heats the water so it boils and makes steam. The steam would like to take up a lot more space than the water but it is squashed into the boiler and cannot escape. This means its pressure has to rise. The boiler has to be very strong to hold it in.

The driver and fireman of a locomotive need to know how much steam pressure is inside the boiler. Too low and the engine will not pull the train. Too high and the safety valves will lift and waste steam and the coal used to make it. They have a pressure gauge.

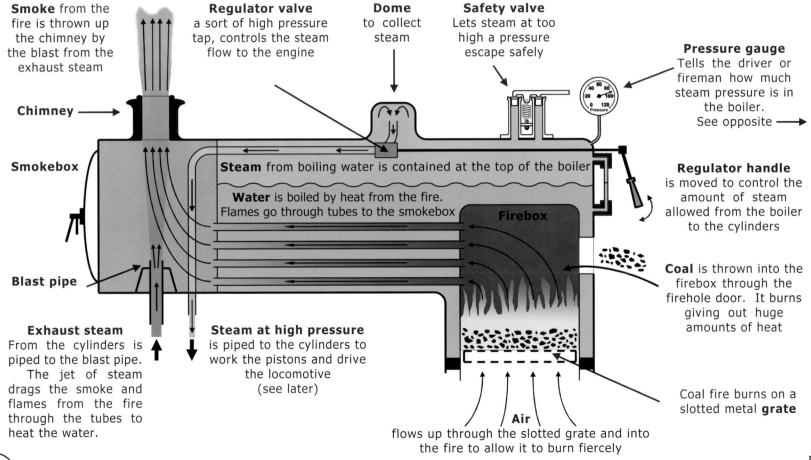

Smoke from the fire is thrown up the chimney by the blast from the exhaust steam

Regulator valve a sort of high pressure tap, controls the steam flow to the engine

Dome to collect steam

Safety valve Lets steam at too high a pressure escape safely

Pressure gauge Tells the driver or fireman how much steam pressure is in the boiler. See opposite ——→

Chimney ——→

Smokebox

Steam from boiling water is contained at the top of the boiler

Water is boiled by heat from the fire. Flames go through tubes to the smokebox

Firebox

Regulator handle is moved to control the amount of steam allowed from the boiler to the cylinders

Blast pipe

Coal is thrown into the firebox through the firehole door. It burns giving out huge amounts of heat

Exhaust steam From the cylinders is piped to the blast pipe.
The jet of steam drags the smoke and flames from the fire through the tubes to heat the water.

Steam at high pressure is piped to the cylinders to work the pistons and drive the locomotive (see later)

Coal fire burns on a slotted metal **grate**

Air flows up through the slotted grate and into the fire to allow it to burn fiercely

Inside the Bourdon Tube Pressure Gauge

Invented by Eugene Bourdon in 1849, it contains a special curved tube which straightens out slightly with steam, gas or water pressure on the inside.

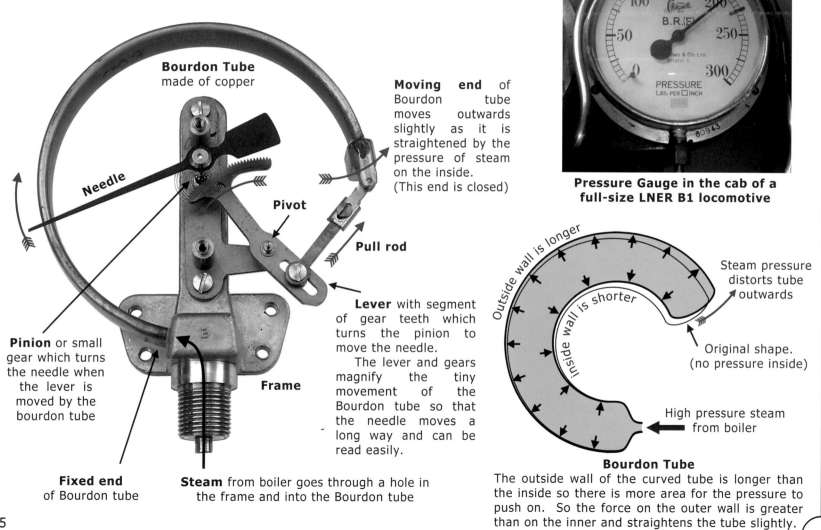

Pressure Gauge in the cab of a full-size LNER B1 locomotive

Bourdon Tube
made of copper

Needle

Pivot

Pull rod

Moving end of Bourdon tube moves outwards slightly as it is straightened by the pressure of steam on the inside.
(This end is closed)

Lever with segment of gear teeth which turns the pinion to move the needle.

The lever and gears magnify the tiny movement of the Bourdon tube so that the needle moves a long way and can be read easily.

Pinion or small gear which turns the needle when the lever is moved by the bourdon tube

Frame

Fixed end of Bourdon tube

Steam from boiler goes through a hole in the frame and into the Bourdon tube

Outside wall is longer

Inside wall is shorter

Steam pressure distorts tube outwards

Original shape.
(no pressure inside)

High pressure steam from boiler

Bourdon Tube
The outside wall of the curved tube is longer than the inside so there is more area for the pressure to push on. So the force on the outer wall is greater than on the inner and straightens the tube slightly.

P 55

Making Tracks

It was time to start making the track for the extension. The lengths of steel rail had been delivered and together with sundry other materials, it was all stacked neatly outside the barn.

Also outside was a huge heap of ballast stones to spread on the levelled ground to make a firm bed for the track.

The first job was to make the thousands of wooden sleepers.

Last time, Mr Plank had cut up a tree for them at his saw mill. However this time he was very busy and did not have the time to help them. They had found another fallen oak tree, it was just a question of how to cut it up.

One morning they were busy setting up the barn as a temporary workshop for making track. Grandpa was in the back part of the barn, behind Mighty Atom, when he found something under a tarpaulin.

"Come and look at this," he shouted. "You might be able to think of a use for what I have just found."

Peter rushed over to see what all the commotion was about. There was Grandpa wreathed in smiles, pointing at an old circular saw bench. It could be driven by a belt from Mighty Atom's flywheel.

"You've struck gold," laughed Peter. "That is just what we need. And even better, it will give Mighty Atom something really useful to do for us."

They could use her to pull the heavy tree out of the wood and then to drive the saw mill.

"I think," Grandpa added, "we will need someone to help us. We can cut the tree up into sections with a chain saw, but they will still be too heavy for you and I to manage on our own."

"Why don't we ask Cara's Dad, Steve," Peter suggested. "He is certainly big and strong. But let's hope he doesn't bring William with him this time. I don't think William and circular saws would be a good combination!"

The next morning, Steve was there bright and early. They had tempted him with the offer of one of Grandma's special cooked breakfasts.

Peter and Grandpa had got up even earlier than usual so they could light Mighty Atom's fire. By the time they went in for breakfast it was already burning brightly and the steam pressure was starting to rise.

Breakfast finished, it was time to get to work. They went outside and found Mighty Atom had just reached full working pressure. They had already oiled all the motion and filled her water tanks so she was ready for the day's work.

They set off with Grandpa at the regulator, Peter at the steering wheel and Steve riding on the trailer behind.

Up at the wood, they uncoupled the trailer and attached a strong metal chain between the fallen tree and the back of the traction engine. Then Grandpa selected the lowest gear so she would have the strongest pull and opened the regulator. The flywheel started to turn and the traction engine moved forwards very slowly, taking up the slack in the chain.

As it pulled tight, Grandpa opened the regulator more until the engine was working really hard. Each beat of the exhaust made a noise like a gun being fired up the chimney as she slowly but steadily hauled the big tree out of the wood and into the field.

Once the tree was out in the open, Grandpa could get at it with the chainsaw. He cut off all the small branches and then cut the trunk into sections which they could winch onto the trailer. The straight bits of the trunk would make the sleepers, the rest would be used for firewood.

Back at the yard, they uncoupled the trailer from the engine and then dragged out the saw bench. Having positioned its pulley in line with the flywheel on the engine, Grandpa connected the two together with a long drive belt.

Then he climbed up on Mighty Atom and connected a much smaller belt between her crankshaft and a little device on the top of the cylinder. It was called a governor and had small weights which spun round and round.

"What does that do?" asked Steve.

"The governor," explained Grandpa, "controls or governs the speed of the engine when driving things by belt. As we feed the logs into the saw it will take a lot more power to keep it spinning and it will start to slow the engine down. The governor will notice the speed dropping and open the steam valve automatically to keep the speed up."

They were ready to start.

"Stand back from the saw," shouted Grandpa. "It's very dangerous and we don't want any fingers or arms being cut off!"

He put the gears in neutral, opened the regulator and the engine started to turn. The saw started to spin as well, but much faster than the engine. It made a dangerous whirring and hissing sound as its teeth sliced through the air.

Grandpa and Steve lifted the first section of the tree onto the saw and fed it into the spinning blade. There was a terrific noise as the teeth ripped through the wood. Mighty

Atom had to work hard to keep the saw spinning but her speed never dropped, thanks to the cunning governor.

There were lots of the large logs to cut up and over 4000 sleepers to make, but by the end of the day they were finished. Mighty Atom never once faltered.

The next job was for Peter to drill all the holes in the sleepers for the screws to hold the rails down. He did it the same way as last time, using the little jig to get all the holes in the right place. It took a whole day.

Then for the rest of the week, Peter and Grandpa assembled the track panels in the barn. Each one was 3 metres long, had 15 sleepers and 60 screws. The extension, including the loop, was 800 metres long so they needed 270 lengths.

They soon got a system going: Lay out the sleepers on the bench. Lay the two rails on the sleepers. Put in the screws either side of the rails to hold them down. Again and again and again......

They would also need two sets of points for the extension. One was needed at the farm, where the new line left the old one. The other set would be needed at the far end where the turning loop joined back onto the line. In the evenings, when Peter had gone home to Woodland Cottage, Grandpa worked on his own in the workshop, making them with great care and skill.

"I have finished making the points," he told Peter one evening. "Tomorrow we can start digging out the track bed."

Drive Belts and the Saw Bench

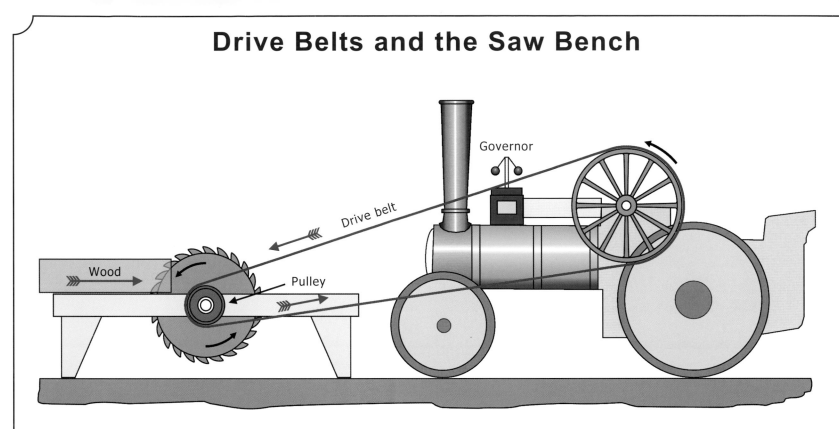

The traction engine is driving the circular saw with a flexible drive belt (red) from the flywheel (green) on its crankshaft. The pulley on the saw is a quarter the size of the flywheel/pulley on the engine so the saw rotates at 4 times the speed of the engine. This high speed is necessary for the saw to cut the wood effectively.

The drive belt works by friction between the pulley and the belt. If too much power is transmitted through the belt, it will eventually slip. This can be an advantage because the belt will slip before damage is done to the machine. If gears are used, slipping is not possible and the teeth may be stripped or some other part of the machine damaged.

In the example here, a long belt is useful because it can transmit the power over some distance to reach the saw.

As the wood is pushed into the saw to cut it, the power required from the engine increases a lot. The governor is always watching and controlling the speed of the engine and adjusting the steam valve to keep the speed constant. When the wood is being pushed into the saw, the governor opens the valve more, to keep the speed up.

When the cut is finished, the engine will start to speed up. The governor will notice this and reduce the flow of steam to keep the speed constant.

The Governor

A device to keep the speed of an engine constant when its load changes

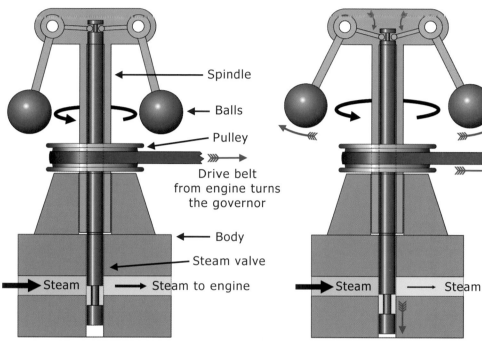

Spindle

Balls

Pulley

Drive belt
from engine turns
the governor

Body

Steam valve

Steam → Steam to engine

Steam → Steam

Steam → Steam

Correct speed

The governor is rotated by a belt from the engine's crankshaft so that as the engine's speed goes up and down, so does the speed of the governor.

The faster the governor spins, the more the balls (red) fly outwards with 'centrifugal force'.

Here the engine is running at the right speed and the steam valve (purple) is partly open.

Too fast

Now the engine is running too fast and the governor weights (red balls) have been flung out further. Their pink fingers have pushed the valve spindle (purple) down, reducing the flow of steam to the engine so that it will slow down.

If you hold a conker on a string and spin it round below your hand, you will see that the faster it spins, the further out it is flung.

Too slow

The engine has now slowed down too much. This would happen when the wood is being pushed into the saw.

The balls have moved inwards because they are spinning round more slowly and their fingers (pink) have lifted the valve (purple) right up.

The valve is now wide open giving full flow of steam to drive the engine at full power.

Building the Yockletts Line

The route to Yockletts bridge was all marked out with stakes, hammered into the ground. The two railway builders now had to dig out some earth to make the bed for the track.

Grandpa started the old digger, and with its usual roar and clouds of blue smoke, its old diesel engine burst into life. Peter guided Grandpa so the trench was lined up with the stakes and to the correct depth to make it good and level.

To lay the track they used their usual method, taking all the materials to the end of the line by train. Ballast went in the wagon with the trap door and new lengths of track on some flat wagons. They would empty out the ballast, rake it flat, bolt on the next track panel and level it up with the spirit level. Then back for more supplies.

Where the line was on a long curve, they made sure that the track was banked over into the bend. It was quite easy to do; they just lifted the outside rail a bit and pushed some ballast stones under the outer ends of the sleepers. This lifted the outside rail a little and created the super-elevation.

Like most jobs on their railway, laying the track was very hard work but the sun was shining and they really enjoyed it.

One afternoon, while having a well earned cup of tea, Peter said that his little brother Harry had made a terrible fuss this morning about putting his clothes on. It took their mum ages to get him dressed.

"I am sure I was never as difficult as Harry," he said, sounding rather grown up.

"You! Not difficult to dress?" roared Grandpa laughing. "You

were a terror. You would refuse to let anyone put your trousers on. You waggled your little legs about and made it completely impossible to get them into the trouser legs."

"You would scream with laughter the whole time until, one day, your father was cunning and got the better of you."

"Knowing how much you loved railways even when you were tiny, he told you that your legs were trains and the trouser legs were tunnels. Then he would ask you which train was going to win the race through the tunnels. You would hold your legs out and kick them into your trousers as quick as a flash."

Peter had forgotten all about this, but thought it was very funny.

"Never mind about that," said Grandpa. "We had better get back to work. I think we might finish the track this afternoon if we get a move on."

The last job to finish the railway was to build a little station at Yockletts village. They made an exact copy of Gerald's Cross and, beside the river, it looked very pretty.

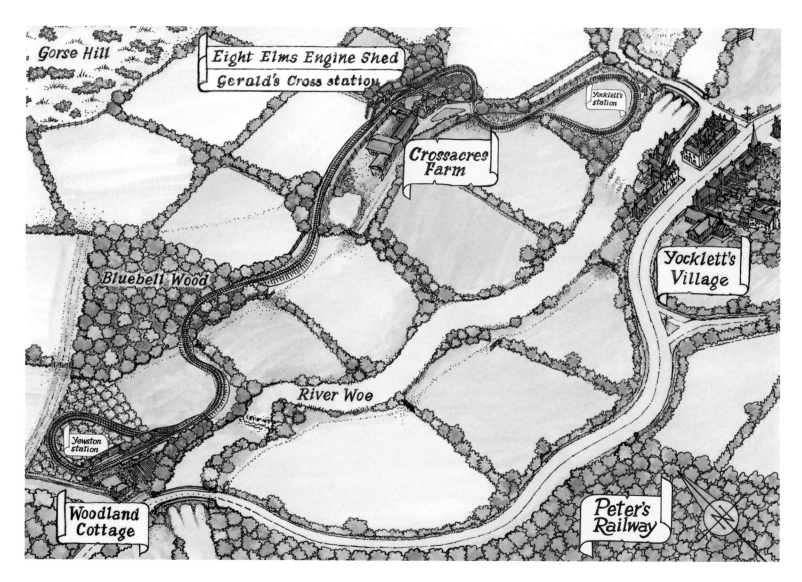

Gorse Hill

Eight Elms Engine Shed

Gerald's Cross station

Yocklett's station

Crossacres Farm

Yocklett's Village

Bluebell Wood

River Woe

Yewston station

Woodland Cottage

Peter's Railway

Banking, Tilting and Super-Elevation

When trains, cars or bicycles go round corners fast, it helps if they are leaning into the bend. All moving objects want to move in a straight line and it takes a large force to make them go round a curve.

The force to push the train round the curve is the rail pushing inwards on the flanges of the wheels. If the train goes too fast it could tip over outwards

If the track is banked over towards the inside of the bend, then gravity helps to keep the train from toppling over outwards.

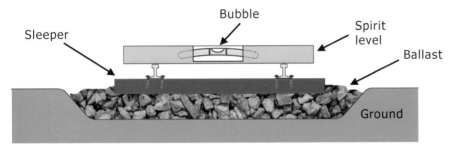

Straight track is set level on the ground. A spirit level is laid across the top of the rails to make sure they are at the same height.

If one rail is higher than the other, the bubble in the spirit level floats towards the higher side.

The engine here is leaning over because the track is banked up at the outside rail.

Gravity is pulling the engine downwards and towards the centre of the bend.

This helps it to go round the curve at high speed.

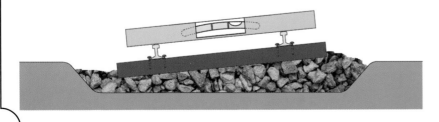

Where the track is on a curve, the outside rail is set higher than the inside so that the trains are tipped, tilted or banked over into the turn.

Here the spirit level is being used to measure how much the track is banked over.

Railway engineers call this 'super-elevation' because one rail is elevated above the other. It is achieved by putting more ballast stones under one end of the sleepers.

This old picture shows a train coming off the old bridge over the Menai Straits between Wales and the island of Anglesey.

The line is on a sharp curve and is clearly banked inwards to help the trains go round it at high speed.

When this bridge was built by Robert Stephenson in 1850, it was one of the great engineering wonders of the world. You can see the pride in the work from the wonderful stone lions which guard the entrance.

Unfortunately stone lions are not very good at guarding things and, in 1970, some boys lit a fire in the bridge and destroyed it.

This much newer picture shows a Virgin Pendolino electric train going fast round a curve.

Again the banking or super-elevation of the track is clearly visible. However these trains can also tilt the carriages so that they lean over even more than the track.

This makes it more comfortable for the passengers because it helps them go round the curve as well! They are less aware of how fast the train is travelling.

These Pendolino trains are designed to operate at speeds of up to 140 mph, whereas the steam engine in the other picture would have struggled to go much faster than 70 or 80 mph.

Newton's First Law of Motion

In 1687, over 300 years ago, Sir Isaac Newton made some fundamental discoveries about how things move. His discoveries are called 'Newton's Laws of Motion' and they explain how everything in the world moves.

His first law of motion is very simple and states that every object either stays at rest or moves at a constant speed in a straight line *unless* a force acts or pushes upon it.

We don't always see this clearly because friction and gravity mess things up. However if you roll a heavy ball across a smooth surface like a bowling alley or snooker table, you will see that it goes in a straight line and does not stop immediately. This is an example of Newton's first law.

It also explains why large forces are needed to make a fast train go round a bend. It really wants to carry on in a straight line and it would do exactly that if the rails did not push sideways on the flanges of the wheels with enormous forces.

Full Steam Ahead to Yockletts

At last they were ready to test out their new and extended railway. They decided to get up steam in the morning and run a few test trains to check that everything worked as intended. Then in the afternoon, they would take Grandma to Yockletts for lunch in the village and to do her shopping for the week.

They had built three special freight wagons to transport Grandma's shopping. Two of them were ordinary wagons, with sides and open tops for most of her shopping. The third one was for carrying chilled and frozen food and was very carefully insulated to keep it cold. It had a hinged lid which doubled up as a long seat if it was needed.

After breakfast, Peter went out to Eight Elms engine shed. After oiling all the parts of the motion and filling the tender with coal and water, he lit the fire. Grandpa coupled up the train and did some odd jobs around the station.

It wasn't long before Fiery Fox had steam up and they were ready. Peter opened the regulator and the train moved slowly out of the station. The first journey on a new line is always interesting, especially if you have built it yourself and are driving a steam locomotive.

Fiery Fox did not have to work hard for the first part of the journey as it was mostly downhill. Peter drove slowly until he was sure of the track, so they had plenty of time to enjoy the view as they cruised along.

Seeing Yockletts station coming into view, Peter closed the regulator and let Fiery Fox coast along the line, gradually slowing down. At the last moment he just touched the brakes and pulled her up to a stop at the new station.

They waited for a few minutes enjoying looking at the river, but it was soon time to carry on with their track testing. Peter put some more coal on the fire and water in the boiler and eased open the regulator for the return trip.

Pulling out of the station, the line started almost immediately on quite a steep climb and the regulator needed to be opened quite a bit more. The track then looped round the edge of the field until it came to the sprung points where it joined back onto the main line from the farm.

Peter was still taking it carefully when they went over the level crossing on the drive and slid round the last few curves and back into the station at the farm.

"Well that was a great success," said Grandpa with a smile. "There's no need to turn the engine on the turntable for the next test trip. We can just run down the line to Woodland Cottage and round the turning loop. We will enjoy the journey and it will be just as quick."

They carried on testing, doing circuit after circuit, each time a little faster. If they noticed a small bump in the track, they stopped and levelled it out.

By lunchtime, they had got the new track perfect. It was very smooth and the banking (or super-elevation if Grandma was within earshot) worked a treat. Peter found that he hardly needed to slow down at all for the curves, the train just leaned into the bends and charged round them.

Back at the Gerald's Cross station, Peter blew some loud blasts on the steam whistle and Grandma came out of the house for her expedition.

When she was safely installed in her saloon carriage, Peter drove the train slowly down the line.

Grandma really enjoyed the journey. It was very pretty when the River Woe came into view, with the new station this side and the village beyond.

When the train had stopped safely at Yockletts station, she got off and walked over the bridge, into the village. She was meeting some friends for lunch and would do her shopping afterwards.

Peter and Grandpa stayed with the train and pottered about doing this and that. They had by now discovered there was always lots of *this* and even more of *that* to do on a railway!

When they thought she would have finished her shopping, they walked into the village to help her carry all the bags back to the waiting train.

When everything was loaded up and Grandma was back in her carriage, Peter blew the whistle and opened the regulator. It was a steep gradient up to the farm from Yockletts and Peter found with the extra weight of the shopping, he had to open the regulator fully and charge the bank at speed.

The exhaust steam barked out of Fiery Fox's chimney like a machine gun as she hauled the heavy train up the incline, gathering speed all the time.

By the time they got to the level crossing they were going at a terrific lick and the train tore round the curves and into Gerald's Cross station. Peter had to put the brakes on fully to stop in time and hoped that Grandma would not have been scared.

They all got off the train and, luckily, Grandma was beaming with smiles.

"That was really wonderful," she said. "I don't think I have ever got home from Yockletts so quickly!"

"I also loved the way my carriage leaned into the bends," she added. "It was just like the brilliant train I went to Scotland in. Whatever was it called?"

"I've got it," she remembered. "It was a Pendulumino."

Peter and Grandpa winked at each other, it was really called a Pendolino but Grandpa just said "Yes Dear."

The Great Railway Race

After the successful day of testing and the shopping expedition, Grandpa and Peter were talking about some sort of party to celebrate their new line.

"We always have a party," said Peter. "I wonder if there is something else we could do to mark the occasion?"

"We've built such a good railway, do you think other people would like to bring their engines here, to drive on our track?" he asked.

Grandpa thought this was a good idea. "I am sure they would love to," he agreed. "Our line is so carefully built they will be able to drive their engines really fast."

"How about a train race then?" suggested Peter. "Most small railways have a speed limit of 10 miles an hour, but we don't have a maximum line speed. They could go as fast as they like!"

Grandpa thought carefully about this. They couldn't race directly, one engine against another, because they didn't have two tracks running next to each other. But they could time how long each engine took to complete a circuit of the railway and the fastest would win.

To fix it all up, they wrote a letter to be printed in the model engineering magazines, asking if anyone with a suitable locomotive would like to visit them for a day of locomotive racing.

While they waited for replies, they made a few preparations for the great event. They built a few extra sidings on the turntable which could be used for holding engines while they were getting up steam. One of them was extended a little into the field beyond so that engines could be unloaded from cars and trailers onto the railway.

One evening Grandpa telephoned to ask Mr Esmond if he would allow Fiery Fox to take part in the race.

"It's a bit dangerous," said Mr Esmond. "And I would hate to see something awful happen. Fiery Fox might come off the track at high speed and be wrecked."

"But, on the other hand," he added quickly, "it will be so exciting to see her running flat out, that I just can't say no."

Once their letter was printed in the magazines, the telephone never stopped ringing. They could not believe how many people wanted to try their locomotives out at high speed.

The competitors arrived with their engines on the Friday evening and soon there were caravans and tents all over the field by the railway. The engines were unloaded and parked on various sidings, ready for the next day.

Peter had noted everyone's name and made up a running list so they all knew the time for their run. He and Fiery Fox would go last.

Some of the engines looked like really fast machines, but Peter had come up with a cunning and secret plan to make Fiery Fox go even faster than usual.....

Saturday morning dawned bright and sunny and everyone was up early, polishing their engines or 'steeds' as Grandma called them. She had moved all of the sheep and cows away from the railway so they would not be hit by speeding trains.

Mr Esmond had come along to watch and was very excited. He was also a bit nervous. After all, if his lovely Fiery Fox came off the track it would be a complete wreck.

All the runs would start at Gerald's Cross, running towards to Woodland Cottage. They would go round the loop without stopping and then back the full length of the line to Yockletts. Then round the loop there and back to the finishing line at Gerald's Cross. A total distance of just over two miles.

The first run was set for noon, so there was plenty of time during the morning for the engines and drivers to get used to driving on the railway. They could learn where the gradients and bends were.

Grandma had agreed to be timekeeper and was sitting on the bench at the station with a stopwatch and clipboard to write down all the results.

At last it was midday and time to start.

The first engine was called 'Slogger', a tank engine with small wheels and not really designed for high speed. But with a full head of steam and a bright fire, her driver was ready.

"3... 2... 1... GO!" shouted Grandma.

The driver wrenched Slogger's regulator wide open. Her wheels spun round and round, slipping madly on the rails and she shot out of the station in a blur of machinery.

"Good gracious!" exclaimed Grandpa. "He was rather rough with his engine. I wonder if he made it himself and knows how to mend it when it breaks?"

"Or maybe he bought it, ready-made," said Peter, "and doesn't know how difficult it will be to mend."

"Either way," chuckled Grandpa, "I shall be amazed if he makes it round the circuit without the whole thing shaking itself to bits."

They waited at the station and about eight minutes later, Slogger reappeared back from Woodland Cottage. Her wheels were still a blur, she was going flat out and her driver's face was covered in oil and soot.

Then as quickly as she had arrived, she was gone again and they all had to wait for her return from Yockletts to the finishing line.

They waited and they waited. What had gone wrong?

After what seemed an age, Slogger wheezed back into Gerald's Cross station and clattered across the finish line. She was still working, but only just. All her bearings were worn out and her pistons were leaking a lot of steam. Her driver didn't seem to mind though, at least he had finished the course.

Grandma announced the time: "16 minutes and 37 seconds."

"I think if he had taken it a bit more steadily," whispered Grandpa to Peter, "and not thrashed his engine, he would have finished much quicker."

They were interrupted by locomotive number two, 'Invicta', puffing up to the start line.

Invicta was a model of a real old timer. She had a long tall chimney and large wheels. At the back of her tender was a wooden barrel to hold the water for the boiler. She looked very old fashioned and had a matching driver; a very old gentleman with white hair.

"3... 2... 1... GO," called Grandma again.

The white haired old gentleman carefully opened Invicta's regulator and they glided out of the station with no fuss at all. They gathered speed slowly and were going at a good pace by the time they disappeared from sight.

When they came back through the station, on their way to Yockletts, they were going at a cracking pace. She was working hard but everything was in good order because she was being driven sensibly and within her limits.

Would they complete the course at this speed, without breaking down?

Everyone waited for old Invicta to come back from Yockletts. They heard her approaching before they could see her. First there was the fast but steady beat of her exhaust and then she came sailing round the bend into the station. The old man was smiling contentedly and Invicta was still running perfectly. They crossed the line in fine style.

"10 minutes and 22 seconds," announced Grandma, writing it down on her clipboard. "Much faster than the last run."

After Invicta, there were lots more engines running. Some were large and powerful looking. Some were small and delicate. Some went like the wind and some were quite slow.

One driver ran out of coal half way round and had to be rescued by another engine. Grandpa said it reminded him of a driver called Sparrow, many years ago. He always took as little coal in the tender as possible. The trouble was that he kept running out and had to borrow coal from the stations and signal boxes along the line.

Next was a lovely model of an old fashioned Stirling Single. She had only a single driving wheel on each side, but it was enormous. As she left the starting line with the train behind her, the huge wheels turned very gracefully and slowly even though she was going quite fast. She was making good time and running well until she came to one of the long uphill gradients. Then she had the same problem that the original full-size engines had over 100 years ago. She started to slip on the rails. The trouble was that most of her weight was on the carrying wheels and there was not enough on the driving wheels to make them grip the rails. Some of the spectators had to give her a little push and so, sadly, she was disqualified.

Grandma sang out the times as the competitors crossed the finishing line. "10 minutes and 5 seconds...... 9 minutes and 26 seconds....."

The times were getting faster. Would Peter ever be able to beat them with Fiery Fox?

Then came a beautiful model of Mallard, the fastest steam locomotive in the world. She had large wheels for fast running and three cylinders to give her extra power. Her driver didn't say much but it was obvious he knew what he was doing.

When Grandma shouted Go, he set off without any slipping but accelerated out of the station very rapidly. Soon he was back again, hurtling through on his way to Yockletts. They didn't have long to wait before he returned and crossed the finishing line in a blur of speed.

"6 minutes and 28 seconds," called out Grandma. "Goodness, that was the fastest yet."

"I was going as fast as I dared," said her driver smiling. "I could have gone even faster but I was worried about the bends on your Yockletts extension. I didn't want to leave the rails and have a crash!"

Peter and Grandpa exchanged glances. "I don't think he realised," said Grandpa quietly, "how carefully we have banked up the track on those curves."

"It's just as well," replied Peter. "He is going to be difficult to beat."

Fiery Fox was ready. Peter had built up the fire with some fresh coal on the hot bed and it was just starting to burn through with bright orange flames.

When Peter drove up to the starting line, everyone was amazed to see that he was lying down instead of sitting up. He was lying partly on the top of Grandma's freezer wagon and partly on the tender itself.

"Why is he doing that?" asked one of the drivers.

"I have no idea," said another. "It looks most uncomfortable."

"He is lying down," explained Grandpa, "to reduce his wind resistance."

All the other drivers had been sitting up, on top of the tenders. But when going fast, there's a lot of drag or wind resistance which the engine has to overcome. By lying down, Peter would reduce his drag and leave more power for the engine to pull the train faster. It was just the same as racing cyclists who crouch down low to go fast.

"3... 2... 1... Go Peter!" shouted Grandma.

Peter opened Fiery Fox's regulator slowly. There were clouds of steam from the cylinder drains but he shut them soon. Fiery Fox gathered speed urgently.

As she got faster, Peter did something that Grandpa had taught him a few days before: He slowly opened the regulator more and wound the reverser back a little, towards mid gear. This was called *notching up* or *linking up* and it meant that Fiery Fox used less steam for the power she was producing. And Peter wanted lots of power!

Soon Fiery Fox was really flying and her exhaust beats had turned into a lovely mechanical purring sound. When Peter opened the firehole door to put on some more coal, he found a raging and savage firestorm inside. The heat was incredible and it reminded him of his cab ride on Green Goddess at the Romney Hythe and Dymchurch Railway.

He had to ease off a bit going round the loop in the orchard at Woodland Cottage, but opened her up fully for the climb back up the gradients to the farm. Only slowing a little for the points in the station, he gave her everything as they flew onto the new track of the extension.

Fiery Fox surged ahead.

Everyone was waiting for him at the finishing line. They heard him first and then saw him as he came charging round the bend by Eight Elms shed and into the station. He crossed the line so fast that it took him quite a distance to stop the train and he had to reverse slowly back to the platform.

Could Peter possibly have beaten Mallard's time of six minutes, 28 seconds?

"And the time for Peter and Fiery Fox is....." Grandma called out, "six minutes and twenty................"

Peter could hardly bear to listen it was so close.

"...... five seconds!" she finished after a dramatic pause.

He had done it. He had won, but it had been too close for comfort. Just three seconds quicker than Mallard.

"Well done," shouted Mr Esmond and Grandpa together. "How did you do it?"

"Well I don't think I went any faster than Mallard on the straights," said Peter. "But when it came to the bends, I knew how carefully we had banked up the track and I just kept the regulator open and held on tight. Fiery Fox did all the hard work and stuck to the rails like glue."

Grandma had put a wooden box on the platform for Peter to stand on when she presented him with his prize.

"Congratulations to Peter and Fiery Fox," she proclaimed. "I proudly announce you the winner of the Great Train Race."

"I have calculated," she added, "that to cover the full circuit of the track in the time you took, you averaged a speed of 20 miles an hour. And at times you must have been going a good deal faster than that."

Then she handed Peter a silver cup which she had won for running when she was a school girl.

Holding the cup above his head, Peter thanked everyone for bringing their engines to the railway.

"There could not have been a race today without you," he finished. "So thank you very much and please visit us again."

Everyone clapped and did three cheers and Peter, blushing happily, stepped down from the box and enjoyed what was left of the day.

Some of the competitors were setting up a giant barbecue and some were enjoying running their locomotives on the railway. Everyone agreed it had been a tremendous success.

When everything had calmed down, Peter, Grandpa and Grandma found themselves back in the kitchen, talking over the events of the day.

Suddenly, and without warning, all the lights went out. They looked out of the window and could see that all the other houses around were also in the dark. It was a power cut. Grandma lit a candle which cast a dim flickering light round the kitchen.

"Wouldn't it be great," said Peter in the gloomy glow, "if we could generate our own electricity. Then we would be the only people with the lights on now."

"Hmmm…" said Grandpa thoughtfully. "It's funny you should say that, because I have been thinking the very same thing."

"Every time I look at the waterfall on the River Woe, I think to myself that it's just begging to have a waterwheel installed there. The waterwheel would drive a generator to power the farm and both our houses. It would be very environmentally friendly and free electricity too."

Once the seed of the idea had been planted, there was not a chance they could forget about it.

"Can we build the waterwheel as our next project?" asked Peter. "Now that would be something really useful."

"It's an excellent scheme. Of course we'll do it," laughed Grandpa. "Just so long as you promise to help me."

That night it took Peter a long time to get to sleep as he was still too excited from the day's racing. But at last he drifted off and spent the night dreaming of the river endlessly turning a waterwheel and the soft hum of generators quietly powering their houses.

But that is another story........

The End.

Pistons and Cylinders and Valves
How the steam turns the wheels and drives the locomotive

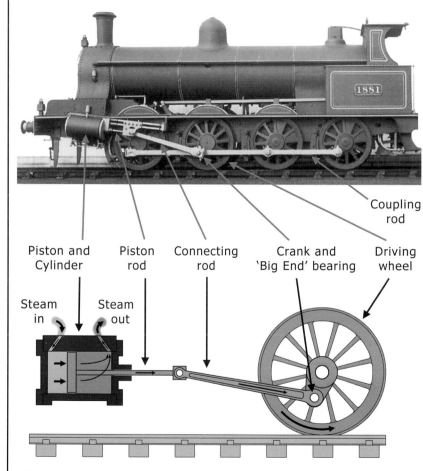

Piston and Cylinder

Piston rod

Connecting rod

Crank and 'Big End' bearing

Driving wheel

Coupling rod

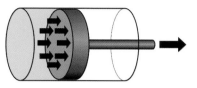

Steam presses on a round piston which is a close sliding fit in the cylinder (a round tube).

The piston and its rod push on the connecting rod which pushes the wheels round. The connecting rod turns the wheels by pushing on a crank, just like a bicycle pedal.

The steam comes from the boiler and is at very high pressure so that it pushes the piston with great force. This is why steam locomotives are so powerful.

Steam in

Steam out

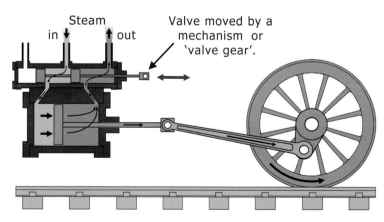

Steam in   out

Valve moved by a mechanism or 'valve gear'.

Steam is let into each end of the cylinder in turn to push and pull the piston. The piston then pushes and pulls on the connecting rod which turns the wheel.

The steam is controlled by a special valve which is moved to allow steam into each end of the cylinder in turn.
The same valve lets the exhaust steam out of the other end.
The valve is moved automatically by an 'eccentric'.

Eccentrics
How the valve moves automatically

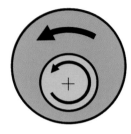

An eccentric is simply a disk of metal (brown) which is mounted off-centre on a shaft (grey). A good word for off-centre is 'eccentric'.

As the shaft rotates the eccentric part moves in a sort of wobbly motion. It works like a mini crank mounted on a shaft.

In many locomotives, eccentrics are set on the axle between the wheels. There is a strap (yellow) in which the eccentric can spin easily. As the wheel, axle and eccentric rotate, the eccentric pushes the strap and the eccentric rod (blue) backwards and forwards. This is the motion which moves the valve.

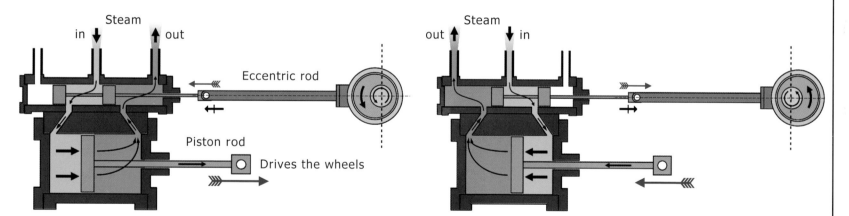

The eccentric has moved the valve from its central position to the left. It is admitting steam to the left end of the cylinder and letting exhaust out of the right end. The piston is pushed to the right.

Now the eccentric has turned through half a turn and moved the valve to the right. Steam flow is reversed and the piston is pushed to the left.

In practice there are two eccentrics for each valve. One is positioned or set for forward running and the other for reverse. There is a system of levers and links to select which one operates the valve and so whether the engine moves forwards or back. This 'valve gear' can also be adjusted by the driver to control the 'cut-off' of the engine to save steam and coal. See next page.

Saving Steam and Coal

Steam in the boiler is at high pressure and very hot. This pressure and heat are valuable forms of energy, put into the steam by burning expensive coal in the firebox of the boiler. The job of the cylinders and pistons is to extract this energy from the steam and turn it into useful work to pull the train, using as little steam as possible. The less steam used, the less coal will be burned.

Long 'Cut-Off' (Train starting)

This sequence shows the valve (green) admitting steam to the cylinder for the whole of the power stroke of the piston.

This means the pressure pushing on the piston stays very high for the whole of its stroke and the engine will work very hard.

The problem is that a lot of steam is used and wasted because it is still at high pressure when the exhaust valve opens and releases it up the chimney.

This situation is needed when the engine is starting and accelerating a heavy train from stopped, or hauling it up a gradient.

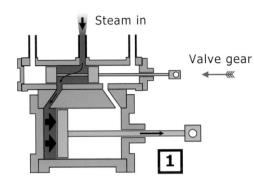

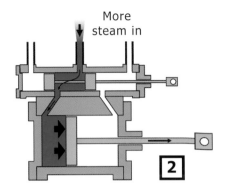

Start of power stroke.
Steam is being admitted, pressure or force on piston is high

Piston pushed to right.
Steam is still being admitted, pressure/force on piston is still high

Short 'Cut-Off' (Train running easily)

In the second sequence, the driver has adjusted the valve mechanism from the cab using the reversing lever (reverser) so that the cut-off point for admitting steam is much earlier in the stroke of the piston.

The steam then expands to push the piston and its pressure drops as the piston moves.

This means the engine will work less hard but will use much less steam and also less coal.

Once the engine has got the train moving, less effort is needed to keep it going, so the driver reduces the cut-off to save steam and coal.

Reducing the cut-off is often known as 'linking up' or 'notching up'.

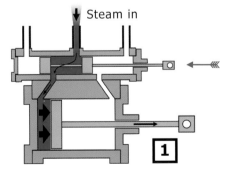

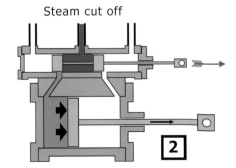

Start of power stroke.
Steam is being admitted, pressure or force on piston is high
(same as above for long cut-off)

Valve (green) cuts off the supply of steam early so very little is used. Steam trapped in the cylinder expands and pushes the piston.

How to use steam more efficiently

More
steam in

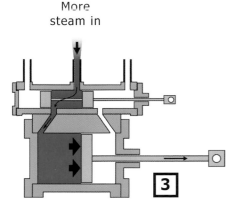

3

Piston pushed further to right.
Steam is still being admitted,
pressure/force on piston is still high

More
steam in

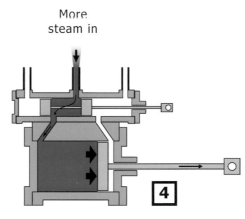

4

Piston pushed to end of stroke.
More steam is still being admitted,
pressure/force on piston is still high.

Steam out,
high pressure
and hot

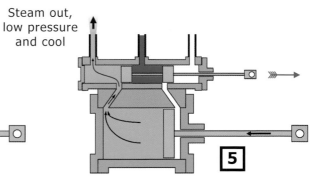

5

Valve (green) has moved to open to exhaust.
Large amount of high pressure and hot steam
is wasted up the chimney.

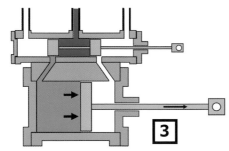

3

As the steam expands and pushes the
piston its pressure drops and it cools
down. It is giving its energy to the
piston to move the train.

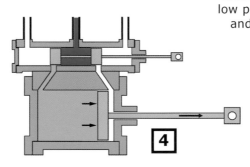

4

By the end of the stroke, the steam
has given up most of its heat and
pressure energy to the piston.
Pressure/force on the piston is lower.

Steam out,
low pressure
and cool

5

Valve (green) has opened to exhaust, letting
low pressure and cool steam up the chimney.
Much less energy is wasted.

Some Special Words

Ballast Rough stones which are put under the track to hold it in place.

Bourdon tube The special curved tube in a pressure gauge, which straightens with pressure inside.

Brake shoe Metal friction block which presses onto the edge of the train wheel to slow it down.

Centrifugal force When an object is made to follow a curved path, it exerts an outward force or centrifugal force. Centrifugal is from Latin and means fleeing from the centre. It is a result of Newton's First Law of Motion because all objects want to move in a straight line; it takes a force to make them go round a curve.

Cylinder Round and smooth tube which contains the piston. The cylinders and pistons are the parts of the locomotive where the power in the steam is converted into the useful motion of the train.

Disc brakes Type of brake where friction pads press on the sides of a disc which is on or behind the wheel. (This is a modern type of brake compared to the type with metal shoes.)

Drain valves (Cylinder drains) Valves to let water escape from the cylinders when they are cold.

Drag (Air resistance) when objects move through air their motion is resisted by the air.

Firebox The metal box which contains the fire. It is completely surrounded by water.

Friction The resistance to motion when one object slides over another and generates heat.

Gear Round wheel with teeth around the edge to mesh with the next gear and turn it.

Gear ratio The relative speed at which one gear rotates compared to another.

Governor Device to keep an engine running at a set speed, even when the load on it changes.

Gradient A slope or hill. On a railway only gentle gradients are used, up to about 1 in 50.

Linking up (Notching up) The valve gear is adjusted from the cab to use steam more efficiently.

Neutral (gear) When gears are in neutral they are not engaged with each other. There is no drive.

Newton, Sir Isaac One of the greatest scientists ever to live. He discovered gravity and also wrote down his 'Laws of Motion'. See page 69 for a description of his first Law of Motion.

Piston valve	A type of valve for controlling the steam in the cylinder. (A slide valve is similar.)
Pulley	A wheel on a shaft for driving or being driven by an endless drive belt.
Pressure	When a lot of steam is squashed into a closed space, its pressure rises. Pressure is often measured in 'pounds per square inch' (or 'psi' for short).
	A pressure of 100 pounds per square inch means that on every square inch of the boiler shell or piston, the steam is pressing with a force of 100 pounds. A square inch is about 6 square centimetres or the area of a 10 pence coin. 100 pounds is about 40 Kilograms or probably the weight of a young person. (The metric unit of pressure is the 'Newton per square Metre' or 'Pascal'. A Newton is a force equal to the weight of about one tenth of a kilogram. 100,000 Pascals is called one 'Bar' and one Bar is equal to about 15 psi in old units. So 100 psi, the working pressure of Fiery Fox, is equal to a pressure of 6.5 Bar.)
Pressure gauge	Device in the locomotive cab which shows the steam pressure in the boiler.
Regulator	Main steam valve used by the driver to control how much steam is used in the cylinders. The more the regulator is opened, the harder and faster the locomotive works. (The regulator is often called the throttle in America.)
Sleepers	Cross beams which hold the metal rails to the correct gauge. ('Ties' in America.)
Spirit Level	Tool for showing if a surface is level by using a bubble in a curved glass tube.
Steam	When water boils it bubbles and turns into steam. Normally steam has a huge volume compared to the water it came from. However in the boiler it is contained in a closed space and so instead of expanding to a large volume, it rises in pressure.
Super-elevation	(Banking) On curves, the outside rail is raised above the inside rail to help with cornering.
Torque	The twisting or turning force (or 'moment') in a shaft or lever.
Traction engine	Old fashioned type of farm tractor, powered by steam. Used to pull things and drive machinery with a belt from its flywheel.
Vacuum	An empty space with nothing in it, not even air. Its pressure is very low or zero.
Water gauge	Device in the locomotive cab which shows the water level in the boiler.

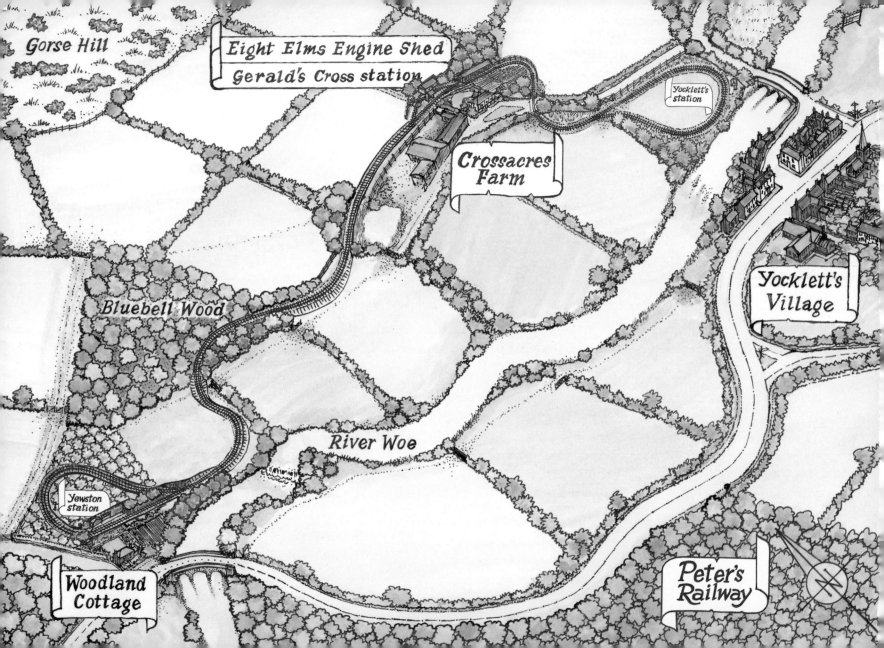

Gorse Hill

Eight Elms Engine Shed
Gerald's Cross station

Yocklett's station

Crossacres Farm

Bluebell Wood

Yocklett's Village

River Woe

Yewston station

Woodland Cottage

Peter's Railway